Maths
made easy

Key Stage 2
ages 10-11
Beginner

Author
John Kennedy

Consultant
Sean McArdle

LONDON • NEW YORK • MUNICH • MELBOURNE • DELHI

Decimal addition

Write the answer to each sum.

$$296.48 + 131.74 = 428.22$$

$$173.05 + 269.23 = 442.28$$

Write the answer to each sum.

$$491.83 + 137.84$$

$$964.71 + 321.26$$

$$302.04 + 204.99$$

$$306.25 + 844.24$$

$$471.93 + 755.26$$

$$842.01 + 711.84$$

$$675.82 + 105.23$$

$$137.82 + 399.71$$

$$465.24 + 605.27$$

$$178.93 + 599.41$$

$$184.74 + 372.81$$

$$443.27 + 705.99$$

$$563.23 + 413.98$$

$$703.95 + 685.11$$

$$825.36 + 249.85$$

$$529.33 + 482.56$$

Write the answer to each sum.

$$421.79 + 136.25 =$$

$$192.31 + 241.73 =$$

$$558.32 + 137.94 =$$

$$501.84 + 361.93 =$$

$$227.66 + 142.07 =$$

$$275.31 + 239.33 =$$

$$153.31 + 189.02 =$$

$$491.44 + 105.37 =$$

$$253.71 + 562.41 =$$

$$829.25 + 163.74 =$$

Problems with negative numbers

What is the difference in temperature between Boston and Barcelona?

11°C

By how much would the temperature have
to go up in Boston to be the same as London?

9°C

City	Temperature
Boston	–9°C
Barcelona	2°C
London	0°C

City	Temperature
Athens	2°C
New York	–6°C
Tokyo	1°C

City	Temperature
Warsaw	–7°C
Zurich	–12°C
Rome	5°C

By how much is Athens warmer than Warsaw?

If the temperature went up by 5°C, what would it be in:

New York   Zurich   Warsaw

If the temperature went down by 6°C, what would it be in:

Tokyo   Rome   Athens

The temperature outside is –11°C. If it rises by 7°C,
what is the new temperature?

The temperature inside a shelter is 5°C.
The temperature outside is 12°C lower.
What is the temperature outside?

The frozen food compartments in a
supermarket are kept at a constant
temperature of –7°C. During a power cut
the temperature rises to 10°C.
By how much has the temperature risen?

The temperature at midnight is –8°C.
At midday it is 15°C higher.
What is the temperature at midday?

Square roots

What is the square root of 9?

> 3

If you do not know the square root of a number you can use the trial method.
What is the square root of 196?

I know the square root of 144 is 12, so it must be bigger than 12.
13 x 13 = 169 (too small)
15 x 15 = 225 (too big)
14 x 14 = 196
The square root of 196 is 14

What is the square root of these numbers? Do your working out on paper if you need to.

16   144   36

4   64   49

81   121   100

Now try these.

324   256   400   289

What length are the sides of these squares?

Area = 361 cm²

Area = 10 000 cm²

         cm   cm

Comparing fractions

Which is bigger, $\frac{2}{3}$ or $\frac{3}{4}$? $\boxed{\frac{3}{4}}$

The common denominator of 3 and 4 is 12.

So $\frac{2}{3} = \frac{8}{12}$ and $\frac{3}{4} = \frac{9}{12}$

$\frac{3}{4}$ is bigger.

Which is bigger?

$\frac{1}{4}$ or $\frac{1}{3}$ ☐ $\frac{5}{6}$ or $\frac{7}{9}$ ☐ $\frac{1}{2}$ or $\frac{5}{8}$ ☐ $\frac{4}{9}$ or $\frac{1}{3}$ ☐

$\frac{2}{5}$ or $\frac{3}{8}$ ☐ $\frac{7}{10}$ or $\frac{8}{9}$ ☐ $\frac{8}{10}$ or $\frac{7}{8}$ ☐ $\frac{7}{12}$ or $\frac{2}{3}$ ☐

$\frac{2}{3}$ or $\frac{5}{8}$ ☐ $\frac{4}{15}$ or $\frac{1}{3}$ ☐ $\frac{3}{5}$ or $\frac{2}{3}$ ☐ $\frac{3}{8}$ or $\frac{1}{4}$ ☐

Which two fractions in each row are equal?

$\frac{1}{4}$ $\frac{3}{8}$ $\frac{4}{12}$ $\frac{3}{12}$ $\frac{7}{8}$ $\frac{5}{8}$

$\frac{5}{8}$ $\frac{6}{9}$ $\frac{7}{10}$ $\frac{8}{12}$ $\frac{1}{2}$ $\frac{3}{4}$

$\frac{7}{12}$ $\frac{6}{14}$ $\frac{7}{14}$ $\frac{3}{8}$ $\frac{4}{8}$ $\frac{9}{12}$

$\frac{3}{8}$ $\frac{3}{9}$ $\frac{2}{6}$ $\frac{4}{7}$ $\frac{9}{10}$ $\frac{6}{7}$

$\frac{3}{10}$ $\frac{5}{15}$ $\frac{2}{10}$ $\frac{3}{15}$ $\frac{4}{10}$ $\frac{7}{15}$

Put these fractions in order starting with the smallest.

$\frac{1}{2}$ $\frac{5}{6}$ $\frac{2}{3}$

$\frac{5}{8}$ $\frac{3}{4}$ $\frac{11}{12}$

$\frac{2}{3}$ $\frac{8}{15}$ $\frac{3}{5}$

Converting fractions to decimals

Convert these fractions to decimals.

$\dfrac{3}{10}$ = $\boxed{0.3}$

(because the three goes in the tenths column)

$\dfrac{7}{100}$ = $\boxed{0.07}$

(because the seven goes in the hundredths column)

Convert these fractions to decimals.

$\dfrac{6}{10}$ = _____ $\dfrac{9}{100}$ = _____ $\dfrac{4}{100}$ = _____ $\dfrac{6}{100}$ = _____

$\dfrac{4}{10}$ = _____ $\dfrac{2}{10}$ = _____ $\dfrac{1}{10}$ = _____ $\dfrac{7}{100}$ = _____

$\dfrac{8}{100}$ = _____ $\dfrac{5}{10}$ = _____ $\dfrac{7}{10}$ = _____ $\dfrac{8}{10}$ = _____

$\dfrac{2}{100}$ = _____ $\dfrac{5}{100}$ = _____ $\dfrac{1}{100}$ = _____ $\dfrac{3}{10}$ = _____

Convert $\dfrac{1}{4}$ to a decimal.

To do this we have to divide the bottom number into the top.

When we run out of numbers we put in the
decimal point and enough noughts to finish the sum.
Be careful to keep the decimal point in your answer
above the decimal point in the sum.

$$\begin{array}{r} 0.25 \\ 4\overline{\smash{)}1.^{1}0^{2}0} \end{array}$$

Convert these fractions to decimals.

$\dfrac{1}{2}$ = _____ $\dfrac{3}{4}$ = _____ $\dfrac{2}{5}$ = _____ $\dfrac{1}{5}$ = _____

$\dfrac{4}{5}$ = _____ $\dfrac{3}{8}$ = _____ $\dfrac{3}{5}$ = _____ $\dfrac{1}{4}$ = _____

Adding

Work out the answer to each sum.   6541 + 634

First add thousands   6000   = 6000

Then add hundreds   500 + 600 = 1100

Next add tens   40 + 30 =   70

Now add units   1 + 4   =   5

                                          7175

Work out the answer to each sum.

2145 + 1734   4261 + 2537   3745 + 2779

4836 + 2628   3058 + 4884   6263 + 275

Work out the answer to each sum.

There are 2424 car park spaces at a seaside resort.
A field is used for an extra 227 cars.
How many cars can now park at the resort?

A large company has 5642 staff.
If it takes on another 429 staff,
how many does it have altogether?

Adding

Work out the answer to each sum.

```
   277            1243
+ 3122           +  62
─────────        ─────────
  3399            1305
                    1
```

Remember to carry if you need to.

Work out the answer to each sum.

```
    241              936              805
+  3781           + 4126           + 5024
───────          ───────          ───────
```

```
    632              807              299
+  4289           + 3424           + 2720
───────          ───────          ───────
```

```
   5319             6402             7065
+    46           +   53           +   27
───────          ───────          ───────
```

Write the answer in the box.

5926 + 75 = ⬚   4813 + 96 = ⬚

327 + 1650 = ⬚   748 + 6913 = ⬚

65 + 8642 = ⬚   4310 + 95 = ⬚

Work out the answer to each sum.

A burger bar sells 3 247 meat burgers and
520 vegeburgers. How many burgers
does it sell altogether?

57 people arrive early for a rugby match.
Later, another 8 642 people arrive. How
many people watch the match?

Subtracting

> Work out the answer to each sum.
>
> $^{6}\,7^{1}2^{1}1$
> $-\quad 52$
> $\overline{669}$
>
> $^{7}3\,8^{1}4^{3}3$
> $-\quad 295$
> $\overline{3\,548}$

Work out the answer to each sum.

581	625	319	847
− 92	− 47	− 36	− 74

934	629	848	516
− 57	− 81	− 99	− 77

Write the answer in the box.

526 − 28 =

192 − 48 =

217 − 78 =

346 − 57 =

Work out the answer to each sum.

222	531	694	382
− 45	− 65	− 78	− 91

428	681	893	156
− 62	− 58	− 47	− 69

Work out the answer to each sum.

A school library has 863 books. If 77 are out
on loan, how many are left on the shelves?

A beach attendant has 587 deckchairs. If 95
are on loan, how many does he have left?

More subtracting

Work out the answer to each sum.

$$
\begin{array}{r}
^3\!\!\not{4}\,^1\!\!\not{2}\,^1\!6\,^1\!5 \\
-\ \ 576 \\
\hline
3\,689
\end{array}
\qquad
\begin{array}{r}
1\,^6\!\not{7}\,^1\!2\,^1\!4 \\
-\ \ \ \ 69 \\
\hline
1\,655
\end{array}
$$

Work out the answer to each sum.

3 932	5 432	6 553	4 117
− 954	− 568	− 491	− 325

7 592	4 346	7 288	6 475
− 885	− 739	− 406	− 131

4 711	2 659	4 437	5 999
− 105	− 532	− 849	− 732

6 337	1 414	2 939	1 216
− 56	− 49	− 87	− 99

6 594	3 253	1 478	2 387
− 95	− 64	− 88	− 98

Work out the answer to each sum.

8 436 people write in for tickets to see a TV show. 750 people receive tickets. How many people don't get a ticket?

5 642 people start a marathon race. 199 people do not finish. How many people cross the finishing line?

Subtracting with 0 on top

Work out the answer to each sum.

$$\begin{array}{r} 4\,^{4}5^{1}0 \\ -\ \ 27 \\ \hline 423 \end{array} \qquad \begin{array}{r} 3\,^{5}6^{1}4^{3}0^{1} \\ -\ 546 \\ \hline 3\,094 \end{array}$$

Work out the answer to each sum.

560 − 26	390 − 34	420 − 16	330 − 25	430 − 114
720 − 319	850 − 526	680 − 351	520 − 134	940 − 455
810 − 247	730 − 141	5 230 − 143	9 520 − 206	8 140 − 128
3 630 − 444	2 370 − 425	8 730 − 826	4 210 − 317	3 580 − 656
4 360 − 574	7 210 − 325	5 480 − 694	9 670 − 795	7 210 − 843
8 540 − 564	2 640 − 645	1 110 − 113	6 340 − 2 555	7 230 − 6 452
5 420 − 3 434	7 650 − 6 998	9 730 − 2 843	6 820 − 1 752	3 590 − 1 591

Real life problems

Work out the answer to each sum.

A farmer's herd of cows produces
245 litres of milk. If he has 97
litres left, how much did he sell?

148 litres

$$\begin{array}{r} {}^{1}3{}^{1} \\ 2\cancel{4}5 \\ -\ 97 \\ \hline 148 \end{array}$$

A farmer has 97 litres of milk.
His herd produces another 127 litres.
How much does he now have?

224 litres

$$\begin{array}{r} 97 \\ +\ 127 \\ \hline 224 \\ {}_{1\ 1} \end{array}$$

Work out the answer to each sum.
Sally buys 3 boxes of chocolates weighing 650 g,
575 g, and 345 g. What is the total weight of
the chocolates?

A car has a full tank of 26.95 litres of petrol. If
a journey uses up 12.47 litres, how much petrol
will be left in the tank?

In a science experiment to test friction Frank is
testing how far different model cars will roll down
a ramp. Car A travels 95.47 cm, car B travels
83.32 cm, and car C travels 72.21 cm.

How much further does car A travel than car B?

How much further does car B travel than car C?

At the end of the experiment, what would the
distance be between car A and car C?

What is the total distance travelled by the three
cars?

Real life problems

A car travels 85 km from town A to town B and 356 km from town B to town C. How far is the total journey?

441 km

```
    85
+  356
   441
   1 1
```

How much greater is the distance between town B and town C than the distance between town A and town B?

271 km

```
   2 1
   356
-   85
   271
```

Work out the answer to each sum.
Mr Barrow weighs 87.36 kg. Mrs Barrow weighs 61.95 kg. Their son Andy weighs 49.83 kg.

What is the sum of their weight?

How much more does Mr Barrow weigh than his son?

What is the difference between Mr and Mrs Barrow's weight?

How much more than Mr Barrow is the combined weight of Mrs Barrow and Andy?

Three children make towers out of bricks. Mira's is 127 cm, Daniel's is 57 cm, and Brian's is 69 cm.

What is the total height of the towers made?

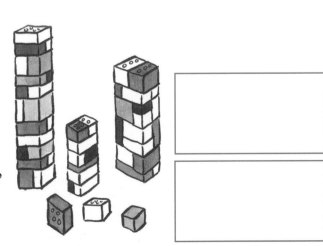

If Brian and Daniel put their towers together, how much shorter will it be than Mira's?

Real life problems

A ship sails 526 km to port A and then 753 km to port B. What is the total distance travelled?

1279 kilometres

$$\begin{array}{r} 526 \\ + 753 \\ \hline 1\,279 \end{array}$$

In a sponsored walk, Sam and Karen walked a combined distance of 19642 metres. If Karen walked 9476 metres how far did Sam walk?

10166 metres

$$\begin{array}{r} 19\,\overset{5}{\cancel{6}}\overset{1}{4}\overset{3}{\cancel{4}}2 \\ - 9\,476 \\ \hline 10\,166 \end{array}$$

Kerry and Sean both make model cars. Kerry's is 65.42 cm long and Sean's is 24.87 cm long. What is the difference in length between their cars?

A sofa costs £845. A table costs £464. How much more is the sofa than the table?

Mr Bonner earns £19426 per year. Mrs Bonner earns £24348 per year. Their daughter Kristy earns £742 a year from her paper round.

What is the total income of the family?

How much more would Kristy need to earn in order to get as much as her mother?

What is the difference between Mr and Mrs Bonner's income?

If Mrs Bonner gave up work, how much money would the family have per year?

Simple use of brackets

Work out these sums.

$(4 + 6) - (2 + 1) =$ $10 - 3 = 7$

$(2 \times 5) + (10 - 4) =$ $10 + 6 = 16$

Remember to work out the brackets first.

Work out these sums.

$(5 + 3) + (6 - 2) =$ ⬚ $(3 - 1) + (12 - 1) =$ ⬚

$(6 - 1) - (1 + 2) =$ ⬚ $(9 + 5) - (3 + 6) =$ ⬚

$(8 + 3) + (12 - 2) =$ ⬚ $(14 + 12) - (9 + 4) =$ ⬚

$(7 - 2) + (4 + 5) =$ ⬚ $(9 - 3) - (4 + 2) =$ ⬚

Now try these longer sums.

$(5 + 9) + (12 - 2) - (4 + 3) =$ ⬚

$(10 + 5) - (2 + 4) + (9 + 6) =$ ⬚

$(19 + 4) - (3 + 2) - (2 + 1) =$ ⬚

$(24 - 5) - (3 + 7) - (5 - 2) =$ ⬚

$(15 + 3) + (7 - 2) - (5 + 7) =$ ⬚

Now try these. Be careful, the brackets now have multiplication sums.

$(2 \times 3) + (5 \times 2) =$ ⬚ $(3 \times 4) - (2 \times 2) =$ ⬚

$(7 \times 2) + (3 \times 3) =$ ⬚ $(5 \times 4) - (3 \times 2) =$ ⬚

$(6 \times 4) - (4 \times 3) =$ ⬚ $(9 \times 5) - (4 \times 6) =$ ⬚

$(12 \times 4) - (8 \times 3) =$ ⬚ $(7 \times 4) - (8 \times 2) =$ ⬚

If the answer is 24, which of these sums gives the correct answer? Write the letter in the box.

a $(3 + 5) + (3 \times 1)$ c $(3 \times 5) + (3 \times 3)$ e $(5 \times 7) - (2 \times 5)$

b $(3 \times 5) + (3 \times 2)$ d $(2 \times 5) + (2 \times 6)$ f $(6 + 7) + (12 - 2)$

⬚

Simple use of brackets

Work out these sums.

$(3 + 2) \times (4 + 1) =$ $5 \times 5 = 25$

$(10 \times 5) \div (10 - 5) =$ $50 \div 5 = 10$

Remember to work out the brackets first.

Work out these sums.

$(7 + 3) \quad \times \quad (8 - 4) =$ $(5 - 2) \quad \times \quad (8 - 1) =$

$(9 + 5) \quad \div \quad (1 + 6) =$ $(14 - 6) \quad \times \quad (4 + 3) =$

$(14 + 4) \div (12 - 6) =$ $(9 + 21) \div (8 - 5) =$

$(11 - 5) \quad \times \quad (7 + 5) =$ $(8 + 20) \div (12 - 10) =$

$(6 + 9) \quad \div \quad (8 - 3) =$ $(14 - 3) \quad \times \quad (6 + 1) =$

$(10 + 10) \div (2 + 3) =$ $(9 + 3) \quad \times \quad (2 + 4) =$

Now try these.

$(4 \times 3) \quad \div \quad (1 \times 2) =$ $(5 \times 4) \quad \div \quad (2 \times 2) =$

$(8 \times 5) \quad \div \quad (4 \times 1) =$ $(6 \times 4) \quad \div \quad (3 \times 4) =$

$(2 \times 4) \quad \times \quad (2 \times 3) =$ $(3 \times 5) \quad \times \quad (1 \times 2) =$

$(8 \times 4) \quad \div \quad (2 \times 2) =$ $(6 \times 4) \quad \div \quad (4 \times 2) =$

If the answer is 30, which of these sums gives the correct answer?

a $(3 \times 5) \times (2 \times 2)$ d $(20 \div 2) \times (12 \div 3)$

b $(4 \times 5) \times (5 \times 2)$ e $(5 \times 12) \div (2 \times 5)$

c $(12 \times 5) \div (8 \div 4)$ f $(9 \times 5) \div (10 \div 2)$

If the answer is 8, which of these sums gives the correct answer?

a $(16 \div 2) \div (2 \times 1)$ d $(24 \div 6) \times (8 \div 4)$

b $(9 \div 3) \times (3 \times 2)$ e $(8 \div 4) \times (8 \div 1)$

c $(12 \times 4) \div (6 \times 2)$ f $(16 \div 4) \times (20 \div 4)$

Answer Section with Parents' Notes
Key Stage 2
Ages 10–11
Beginner

This 8-page section provides answers to all the activities in this book. This will enable you to mark your children's work or can be used by them if they prefer to do their own marking.

The notes for each page help explain the common pitfalls and problems and, where appropriate, give indications as to what practice is needed to ensure your children understand where they have gone wrong.

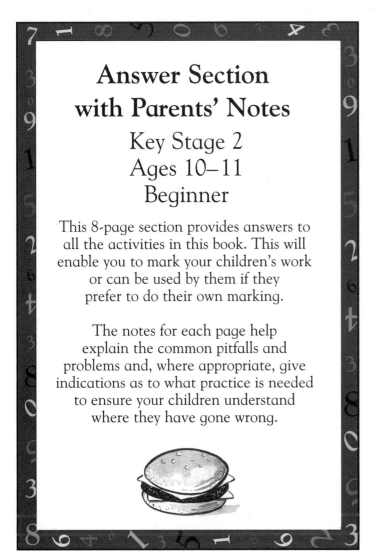

Decimal addition

Write the answer to each sum.

296.48	173.05
+ 131.74	+ 269.23
428.22	442.28

Write the answer to each sum.

491.83	964.71	302.04	306.25
+ 137.84	+ 321.26	+ 204.99	+ 844.24
629.67	1285.97	507.03	1150.49

471.93	842.01	675.82	137.82
+ 755.26	+ 711.84	+105.23	+ 399.71
1227.19	1553.85	781.05	537.53

465.24	178.93	184.74	443.27
+ 605.27	+ 599.41	+ 372.81	+ 705.99
1070.51	778.34	557.55	1149.26

563.23	703.95	825.36	529.33
+ 413.98	+ 685.11	+ 249.85	+ 482.56
977.21	1389.06	1075.21	1011.89

Write the answer to each sum.

421.79 + 136.25 = 558.04   192.31 + 241.73 = 434.04

558.32 + 137.94 = 696.26   501.84 + 361.93 = 863.77

227.66 + 142.07 = 369.73   275.31 + 239.33 = 514.64

153.31 + 189.02 = 342.33   491.44 + 105.37 = 596.81

253.71 + 562.41 = 816.12   829.25 + 163.74 = 992.99

Look out for errors when the child is working horizontally, adding digits with different place values. Less confident children may need to be reassured when carrying across the decimal point.

Problems with negative numbers ☆

What is the difference in temperature between Boston and Barcelona?

11°C

By how much would the temperature have to go up in Boston to be the same as London?

9°C

City	Temperature
Boston	−9°C
Barcelona	2°C
London	0°C

City	Temperature		City	Temperature
Athens	2°C		Warsaw	−7°C
New York	−6°C		Zurich	−12°C
Tokyo	1°C		Rome	5°C

By how much is Athens warmer than Warsaw?   9°C

If the temperature went up by 5°C, what would it be in:

New York −1°C   Zurich −7°C   Warsaw −2°C

If the temperature went down by 6°C, what would it be in:

Tokyo −5°C   Rome −1°C   Athens −4°C

The temperature outside is −11°C. If it rises by 7°C, what is the new temperature?   −4°C

The temperature inside a shelter is 5°C. The temperature outside is 12°C lower. What is the temperature outside?   −7°C

The frozen food compartments in a supermarket are kept at a constant temperature of −7°C. During a power cut the temperature rises to 10°C. By how much has the temperature risen?   17°C

The temperature at midnight is −8°C. At midday it is 15°C higher. What is the temperature at midday?   7°C

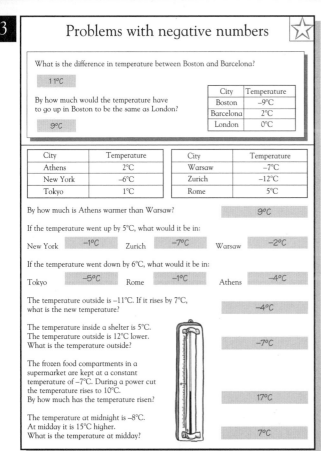

When children add to, or subtract from, negative numbers they may have difficulty understanding why the number appears to get smaller when they add, and larger when they subtract. The use of a number line, e.g. a thermometer, makes the operation clearer.

Square roots

What is the square root of 9?

3

If you do not know the square root of a number you can use the trial method. What is the square root of 196? I know the square root of 144 is 12, so it must be bigger than 12.
13 × 13 = 169 (too small)
15 × 15 = 225 (too big)
14 × 14 = 196
The square root of 196 is 14

What is the square root of these numbers? Do your working out on paper if you need to.

16 4   144 12   36 6

4 2   64 8   49 7

81 9   121 11   100 10

Now try these.

324 18   256 16   400 20   289 17

What length are the sides of these squares?

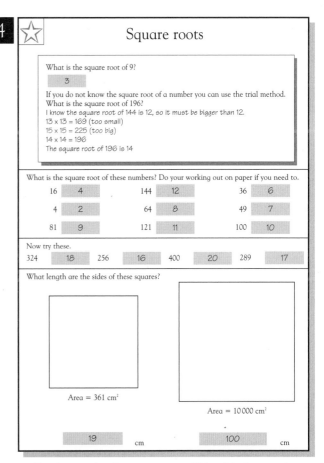

Area = 361 cm²

Area = 10 000 cm²

19 cm   100 cm

Difficulty in the first section will highlight weaknesses in times tables knowledge. In the second and third sections, children should use the trial and improvement method outlined in the example.

Comparing fractions

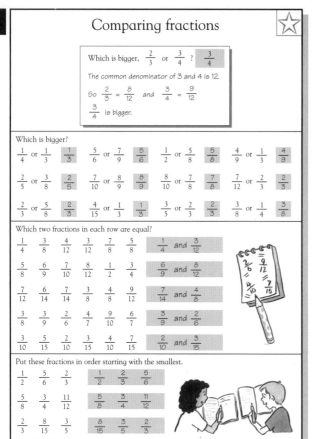

Which is bigger, $\frac{2}{3}$ or $\frac{3}{4}$? $\boxed{\frac{3}{4}}$

The common denominator of 3 and 4 is 12.

So $\frac{2}{3} = \frac{8}{12}$ and $\frac{3}{4} = \frac{9}{12}$

$\frac{3}{4}$ is bigger.

Which is bigger?

$\frac{1}{4}$ or $\frac{1}{3}$ $\boxed{\frac{1}{3}}$ $\frac{5}{6}$ or $\frac{7}{9}$ $\boxed{\frac{5}{6}}$ $\frac{1}{2}$ or $\frac{5}{8}$ $\boxed{\frac{5}{8}}$ $\frac{4}{9}$ or $\frac{1}{3}$ $\boxed{\frac{4}{9}}$

$\frac{2}{5}$ or $\frac{3}{8}$ $\boxed{\frac{2}{5}}$ $\frac{7}{10}$ or $\frac{8}{9}$ $\boxed{\frac{8}{9}}$ $\frac{8}{10}$ or $\frac{7}{8}$ $\boxed{\frac{7}{8}}$ $\frac{7}{12}$ or $\frac{2}{3}$ $\boxed{\frac{2}{3}}$

$\frac{2}{3}$ or $\frac{5}{8}$ $\boxed{\frac{2}{3}}$ $\frac{4}{15}$ or $\frac{1}{3}$ $\boxed{\frac{1}{3}}$ $\frac{3}{5}$ or $\frac{2}{3}$ $\boxed{\frac{2}{3}}$ $\frac{3}{8}$ or $\frac{1}{4}$ $\boxed{\frac{3}{8}}$

Which two fractions in each row are equal?

$\frac{1}{4}$ $\frac{3}{8}$ $\frac{4}{12}$ $\frac{3}{12}$ $\frac{7}{8}$ $\frac{5}{8}$ $\boxed{\frac{1}{4} \text{ and } \frac{3}{12}}$

$\frac{5}{8}$ $\frac{6}{9}$ $\frac{7}{10}$ $\frac{8}{12}$ $\frac{1}{2}$ $\frac{3}{4}$ $\boxed{\frac{6}{9} \text{ and } \frac{8}{12}}$

$\frac{7}{12}$ $\frac{6}{14}$ $\frac{7}{14}$ $\frac{3}{8}$ $\frac{4}{8}$ $\frac{9}{12}$ $\boxed{\frac{7}{14} \text{ and } \frac{4}{8}}$

$\frac{3}{8}$ $\frac{3}{9}$ $\frac{2}{6}$ $\frac{4}{7}$ $\frac{9}{10}$ $\frac{6}{7}$ $\boxed{\frac{3}{9} \text{ and } \frac{2}{6}}$

$\frac{3}{10}$ $\frac{5}{15}$ $\frac{2}{10}$ $\frac{3}{15}$ $\frac{4}{10}$ $\frac{7}{15}$ $\boxed{\frac{2}{10} \text{ and } \frac{3}{15}}$

Put these fractions in order starting with the smallest.

$\frac{1}{2}$ $\frac{5}{6}$ $\frac{2}{3}$ $\boxed{\frac{1}{2} \quad \frac{2}{3} \quad \frac{5}{6}}$

$\frac{5}{8}$ $\frac{3}{4}$ $\frac{11}{12}$ $\boxed{\frac{5}{8} \quad \frac{3}{4} \quad \frac{11}{12}}$

$\frac{2}{3}$ $\frac{8}{15}$ $\frac{3}{5}$ $\boxed{\frac{8}{15} \quad \frac{3}{5} \quad \frac{2}{3}}$

Difficulty in finding a common denominator indicates a weakness in times tables knowledge. Children need to convert all the fractions in the later questions into a common form before answering the question. Be careful that they do not try to guess the answer.

Converting fractions to decimals

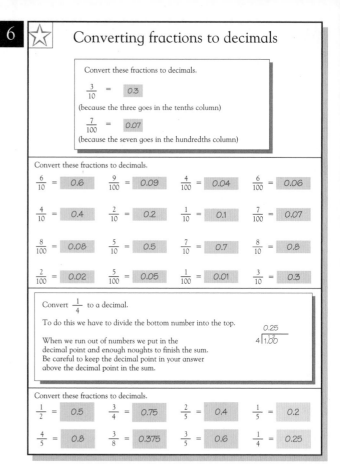

Convert these fractions to decimals.

$\frac{3}{10} = \boxed{0.3}$

(because the three goes in the tenths column)

$\frac{7}{100} = \boxed{0.07}$

(because the seven goes in the hundredths column)

Convert these fractions to decimals.

$\frac{6}{10} = \boxed{0.6}$ $\frac{9}{100} = \boxed{0.09}$ $\frac{4}{100} = \boxed{0.04}$ $\frac{6}{100} = \boxed{0.06}$

$\frac{4}{10} = \boxed{0.4}$ $\frac{2}{10} = \boxed{0.2}$ $\frac{1}{10} = \boxed{0.1}$ $\frac{7}{100} = \boxed{0.07}$

$\frac{8}{100} = \boxed{0.08}$ $\frac{5}{10} = \boxed{0.5}$ $\frac{7}{10} = \boxed{0.7}$ $\frac{8}{10} = \boxed{0.8}$

$\frac{2}{100} = \boxed{0.02}$ $\frac{5}{100} = \boxed{0.05}$ $\frac{1}{100} = \boxed{0.01}$ $\frac{3}{10} = \boxed{0.3}$

Convert $\frac{1}{4}$ to a decimal.

To do this we have to divide the bottom number into the top.

When we run out of numbers we put in the decimal point and enough noughts to finish the sum. Be careful to keep the decimal point in your answer above the decimal point in the sum.

$$4\overline{)1.00} = 0.25$$

Convert these fractions to decimals.

$\frac{1}{2} = \boxed{0.5}$ $\frac{3}{4} = \boxed{0.75}$ $\frac{2}{5} = \boxed{0.4}$ $\frac{1}{5} = \boxed{0.2}$

$\frac{4}{5} = \boxed{0.8}$ $\frac{3}{8} = \boxed{0.375}$ $\frac{3}{5} = \boxed{0.6}$ $\frac{1}{4} = \boxed{0.25}$

Difficulty in the first section highlights weakness in understanding place value to the first two decimal places. It may be necessary to reinforce understanding of 10ths and 100ths in decimals.

Adding

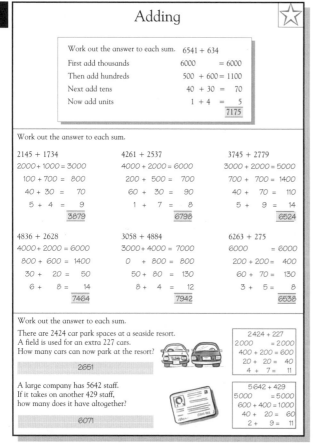

Work out the answer to each sum.   6541 + 634

First add thousands	6000	= 6000
Then add hundreds	500 + 600	= 1100
Next add tens	40 + 30	= 70
Now add units	1 + 4	= 5

$\boxed{7175}$

Work out the answer to each sum.

2145 + 1734
2000 + 1000 = 3000
100 + 700 = 800
40 + 30 = 70
5 + 4 = 9
$\boxed{3879}$

4261 + 2537
4000 + 2000 = 6000
200 + 500 = 700
60 + 30 = 90
1 + 7 = 8
$\boxed{6798}$

3745 + 2779
3000 + 2000 = 5000
700 + 700 = 1400
40 + 70 = 110
5 + 9 = 14
$\boxed{6524}$

4836 + 2628
4000 + 2000 = 6000
800 + 600 = 1400
30 + 20 = 50
6 + 8 = 14
$\boxed{7464}$

3058 + 4884
3000 + 4000 = 7000
0 + 800 = 800
50 + 80 = 130
8 + 4 = 12
$\boxed{7942}$

6263 + 275
6000 = 6000
200 + 200 = 400
60 + 70 = 130
3 + 5 = 8
$\boxed{6538}$

Work out the answer to each sum.

There are 2424 car park spaces at a seaside resort. A field is used for an extra 227 cars. How many cars can now park at the resort?

$\boxed{2651}$

2424 + 227
2000 = 2000
400 + 200 = 600
20 + 20 = 40
4 + 7 = 11

A large company has 5642 staff. If it takes on another 429 staff, how many does it have altogether?

$\boxed{6071}$

5642 + 429
5000 = 5000
600 + 400 = 1000
40 + 20 = 60
2 + 9 = 11

This method of addition is sometimes known as 'chunking' because the work is carried out in groups or chunks. The final stage of finding the total is usually where a child will make a mistake, especially where carrying is needed.

Adding

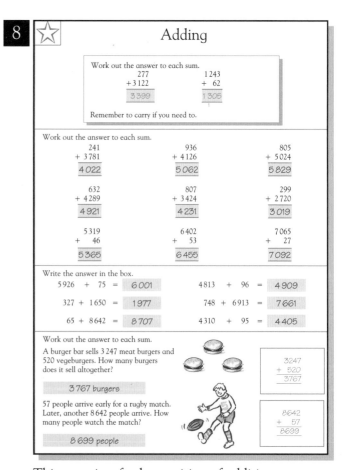

Work out the answer to each sum.

```
  277          1 243
+3 122        +  62
-----         ------
 3 399         1 305
```

Remember to carry if you need to.

Work out the answer to each sum.

```
   241         936          805
+ 3 781      + 4 126      + 5 024
-------      -------      -------
  4 022       5 062        5 829
```

```
   632         807          299
+ 4 289      + 3 424      + 2 720
-------      -------      -------
  4 921       4 231        3 019
```

```
  5 319        6 402        7 065
+   46       +   53       +   27
-------      -------      -------
  5 365       6 455        7 092
```

Write the answer in the box.

5926 + 75 = $\boxed{6\,001}$ 4813 + 96 = $\boxed{4\,909}$

327 + 1650 = $\boxed{1977}$ 748 + 6913 = $\boxed{7\,661}$

65 + 8642 = $\boxed{8\,707}$ 4310 + 95 = $\boxed{4\,405}$

Work out the answer to each sum.

A burger bar sells 3 247 meat burgers and 520 vegeburgers. How many burgers does it sell altogether?

$\boxed{3\,767 \text{ burgers}}$

```
 3247
+ 520
-----
 3767
```

57 people arrive early for a rugby match. Later, another 8 642 people arrive. How many people watch the match?

$\boxed{8\,699 \text{ people}}$

```
 8642
+  57
-----
 8699
```

This page is a further revision of addition.

Subtracting

Work out the answer to each sum.

$$\begin{array}{r} 6\,{}^{1}1 \\ 7\cancel{2}\cancel{1} \\ -\ \ 52 \\ \hline 669 \end{array} \qquad \begin{array}{r} 7\,{}^{3}1 \\ 3\,8\cancel{4}\cancel{3} \\ -\ \ 295 \\ \hline 3\,548 \end{array}$$

Work out the answer to each sum.

581 − 92 = **489**	625 − 47 = **578**	319 − 36 = **283**	847 − 74 = **773**
934 − 57 = **877**	629 − 81 = **548**	848 − 99 = **749**	516 − 77 = **439**

Write the answer in the box.

526 − 28 = **498**   192 − 48 = **144**

217 − 78 = **139**   346 − 57 = **289**

Work out the answer to each sum.

222 − 45 = **177**	531 − 65 = **466**	694 − 78 = **616**	382 − 91 = **291**
428 − 62 = **366**	681 − 58 = **623**	893 − 47 = **846**	156 − 69 = **87**

Work out the answer to each sum.

A school library has 863 books. If 77 are out on loan, how many are left on the shelves?
786 books

$$\begin{array}{r} 7\,{}^{15}1 \\ \cancel{8}\cancel{6}3 \\ -\ \ 77 \\ \hline 786 \end{array}$$

A beach attendant has 587 deckchairs. If 95 are on loan, how many does he have left?
492 deckchairs

$$\begin{array}{r} 4\,1 \\ 5\cancel{8}7 \\ -\ \ 95 \\ \hline 492 \end{array}$$

When a larger digit has to be taken away from a smaller digit children often take the smaller one on the top away from the larger one on the bottom. They should recognise when sums require decomposition, which means 'stealing' from the digit on the left.

More subtracting

Work out the answer to each sum.

$$\begin{array}{r} 3\,{}^{11}\,{}^{15}1 \\ 4\,\cancel{2}\cancel{6}\cancel{5} \\ -\ \ 576 \\ \hline 3\,689 \end{array} \qquad \begin{array}{r} 6\,{}^{1}1 \\ 1\,\cancel{7}\cancel{2}4 \\ -\ \ 69 \\ \hline 1\,655 \end{array}$$

Work out the answer to each sum.

3 932 − 954 = **2 978**	5 432 − 568 = **4 864**	6 553 − 491 = **6 062**	4 117 − 325 = **3 792**
7 592 − 885 = **6 707**	4 346 − 739 = **3 607**	7 288 − 406 = **6 882**	6 475 − 131 = **6 344**
4 711 − 105 = **4 606**	2 659 − 532 = **2 127**	4 437 − 849 = **3 588**	5 999 − 732 = **5 267**
6 337 − 56 = **6 281**	1 414 − 49 = **1 365**	2 939 − 87 = **2 852**	1 216 − 99 = **1 117**
6 594 − 95 = **6 499**	3 253 − 64 = **3 189**	1 478 − 88 = **1 390**	2 387 − 98 = **2 289**

Work out the answer to each sum.

8 436 people write in for tickets to see a TV show. 750 people receive tickets. How many have to watch the show on TV?
7 686

$$\begin{array}{r} {}^{13} \\ 8\,4\cancel{3}6 \\ -\ \ 750 \\ \hline 7\,686 \end{array}$$

5 642 people start a marathon race. 199 people do not finish. How many people cross the finishing line?
5 443

$$\begin{array}{r} 5\,1 \\ 5\,6\cancel{4}2 \\ -\ \ 199 \\ \hline 5\,443 \end{array}$$

The work on this page is similar to the previous page but involves larger amounts and wider differences between the numbers subtracted.

Subtracting with 0 on top

Work out the answer to each sum.

$$\begin{array}{r} 4\,1 \\ 4\cancel{3}\cancel{0} \\ -\ \ 27 \\ \hline 423 \end{array} \qquad \begin{array}{r} 5\,{}^{13}1 \\ 3\,6\cancel{4}\cancel{0} \\ -\ \ 546 \\ \hline 3\,094 \end{array}$$

Work out the answer to each sum.

560 − 26 = **534**	390 − 34 = **356**	420 − 16 = **404**	330 − 25 = **305**	430 − 114 = **316**
720 − 319 = **401**	850 − 526 = **324**	680 − 351 = **329**	520 − 134 = **386**	940 − 455 = **485**
810 − 247 = **563**	730 − 141 = **589**	5 230 − 143 = **5 087**	9 520 − 206 = **9 314**	8 140 − 128 = **8 012**
3 630 − 444 = **3 186**	2 370 − 425 = **1 945**	8 730 − 826 = **7 904**	4 210 − 317 = **3 893**	3 580 − 656 = **2 924**
4 360 − 574 = **3 786**	7 210 − 325 = **6 885**	5 480 − 694 = **4 786**	9 670 − 795 = **8 875**	7 210 − 843 = **6 367**
8 540 − 564 = **7 976**	2 640 − 645 = **1 995**	1 110 − 113 = **997**	6 340 − 2 555 = **3 785**	7 230 − 6 452 = **778**
5 420 − 3 434 = **1 986**	7 650 − 6 998 = **652**	9 730 − 2 843 = **6 887**	6 820 − 1 752 = **5 068**	3 590 − 1 591 = **1 999**

This page is similar to the previous two, but the number on top has a nought in the units column. If children have difficulty, explain that when 'stealing' a digit from the tens column, it goes together with the zero in the units column to make a ten.

Real life problems

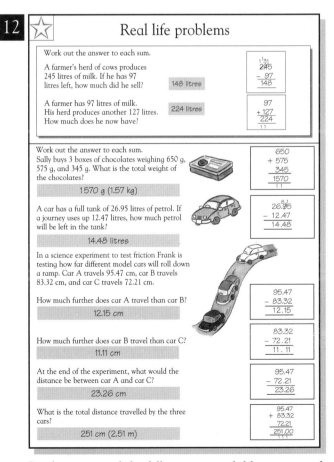

Work out the answer to each sum.

A farmer's herd of cows produces 245 litres of milk. If he has 97 litres left, how much did he sell?
148 litres

$$\begin{array}{r} 1\,{}^{3}1 \\ 2\cancel{4}\cancel{5} \\ -\ \ 97 \\ \hline 148 \end{array}$$

A farmer has 97 litres of milk. His herd produces another 127 litres. How much does he now have?
224 litres

$$\begin{array}{r} 97 \\ +\ 127 \\ \hline 224 \\ {}_{1\ 1} \end{array}$$

Work out the answer to each sum.

Sally buys 3 boxes of chocolates weighing 650 g, 575 g, and 345 g. What is the total weight of the chocolates?
1570 g (1.57 kg)

$$\begin{array}{r} 650 \\ +\ 575 \\ 345 \\ \hline 1570 \\ {}_{1\ 1} \end{array}$$

A car has a full tank of 26.95 litres of petrol. If a journey uses up 12.47 litres, how much petrol will be left in the tank?
14.48 litres

$$\begin{array}{r} 8\,1 \\ 26.\cancel{9}5 \\ -\ 12.47 \\ \hline 14.48 \end{array}$$

In a science experiment to test friction Frank is testing how far different model cars will roll down a ramp. Car A travels 95.47 cm, car B travels 83.32 cm, and car C travels 72.21 cm.

How much further does car A travel than car B?
12.15 cm

$$\begin{array}{r} 95.47 \\ -\ 83.32 \\ \hline 12.15 \end{array}$$

How much further does car B travel than car C?
11.11 cm

$$\begin{array}{r} 83.32 \\ -\ 72.21 \\ \hline 11.11 \end{array}$$

At the end of the experiment, what would the distance be between car A and car C?
23.26 cm

$$\begin{array}{r} 95.47 \\ -\ 72.21 \\ \hline 23.26 \end{array}$$

What is the total distance travelled by the three cars?
251 cm (2.51 m)

$$\begin{array}{r} 95.47 \\ 83.32 \\ +\ 72.21 \\ \hline 251.00 \\ {}_{1\ 1\ 1} \end{array}$$

On this page and the following two, children can apply skills of addition and subtraction to real life problems, using various units of measurement. If they are unsure which operation to use, discuss whether the answer will be larger (addition) or smaller (subtraction).

Real life problems

Work out the answer to each sum.

A car travels 85 km from town A to town B and 356 km from town B to town C. How far is the total journey?   441 km

```
    85
+  356
   441
   1 1
```

How much greater is the distance between town B and town C than the distance between town A and town B?   271 km

```
  2
  356
-  85
  271
```

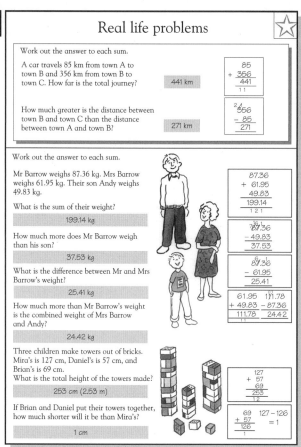

Work out the answer to each sum.

Mr Barrow weighs 87.36 kg. Mrs Barrow weighs 61.95 kg. Their son Andy weighs 49.83 kg.

What is the sum of their weight?   199.14 kg

```
    87.36
  + 61.95
    49.83
   199.14
   1 2 1
```

How much more does Mr Barrow weigh than his son?   37.53 kg

```
  16
  87.36
- 49.83
  37.53
```

What is the difference between Mr and Mrs Barrow's weight?   25.41 kg

```
   8  1
  87.36
- 61.95
  25.41
```

How much more than Mr Barrow's weight is the combined weight of Mrs Barrow and Andy?   24.42 kg

```
   61.95    111.78
 + 49.83  - 87.36
  111.78    24.42
    1 1
```

Three children make towers out of bricks. Mira's is 127 cm, Daniel's is 57 cm, and Brian's is 69 cm.
What is the total height of the towers made?   253 cm (2.53 m)

```
   127
 +  57
    69
   253
    1 2
```

If Brian and Daniel put their towers together, how much shorter will it be than Mira's?   1 cm

```
   69    127 – 126
 + 57      = 1
  126
    1
```

This page again helps children revise their skills of addition and subtraction in real life situations.

Real life problems

A ship sails 526 km to port A and then 753 km to port B. What is the total distance travelled?   1 279 kilometres

```
    526
 +  753
   1 279
```

In a sponsored walk, Sam and Karen walked a combined distance of 19 642 metres. If Karen walked 9 476 metres how far did Sam walk?   10 166 metres

```
    5 13 1
   19 642
 -  9 476
   10 166
```

Kerry and Sean both make model cars. Kerry's is 65.42 cm long and Sean's is 24.87 cm long. What is the difference in length between their cars?   40.55 cm

```
    4 13 1
   65.42
 - 24.87
   40.55
```

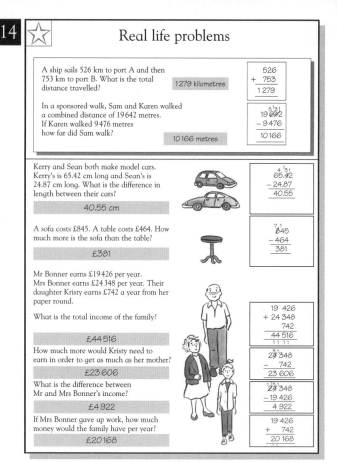

A sofa costs £845. A table costs £464. How much more is the sofa than the table?   £381

```
    7 1
   845
 - 464
   381
```

Mr Bonner earns £19 426 per year. Mrs Bonner earns £24 348 per year. Their daughter Kristy earns £742 a year from her paper round.

What is the total income of the family?   £44 516

```
   19 426
 + 24 348
      742
   44 516
   1 1 1 1
```

How much more would Kristy need to earn in order to get as much as her mother?   £23 606

```
   3 1
   24 348
 -    742
   23 606
```

What is the difference between Mr and Mrs Bonner's income?   £4 922

```
   1 13 1
   24 348
 - 19 426
    4 922
```

If Mrs Bonner gave up work, how much money would the family have per year?   £20 168

```
   19 426
 +    742
   20 168
```

This page too helps children revise their skills of addition and subtraction in real life situations.

Simple use of brackets

Work out these sums.
(4 + 6) – (2 + 1) =   10 – 3 = 7
(2 x 5) + (10 – 4) =   10 + 6 = 16
Remember to work out the brackets first.

Work out these sums.

(5 + 3) + (6 – 2) =   12   (3 – 1) + (12 – 1) =   13

(6 – 1) – (1 + 2) =   2   (9 + 5) – (3 + 6) =   5

(8 + 3) + (12 – 2) =   21   (14 + 12) – (9 + 4) =   13

(7 – 2) + (4 + 5) =   14   (9 – 3) – (4 + 2) =   0

Now try these longer sums.

(5 + 9) + (12 – 2) – (4 + 3) =   17

(10 + 5) – (2 + 4) + (9 + 6) =   24

(19 + 4) – (3 + 2) – (2 + 1) =   15

(24 – 5) – (3 + 7) – (5 – 2) =   6

(15 + 3) + (7 – 2) – (5 + 7) =   11

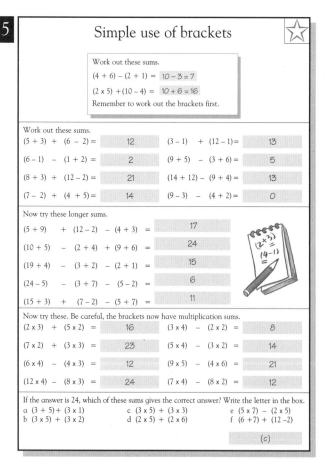

Now try these. Be careful, the brackets now have multiplication sums.
(2 x 3) + (5 x 2) =   16   (3 x 4) – (2 x 2) =   8

(7 x 2) + (3 x 3) =   23   (5 x 4) – (3 x 2) =   14

(6 x 4) – (4 x 3) =   12   (9 x 5) – (4 x 6) =   21

(12 x 4) – (8 x 3) =   24   (7 x 4) – (8 x 2) =   12

If the answer is 24, which of these sums gives the correct answer? Write the letter in the box.
a (3 + 5) + (3 x 1)   c (3 x 5) + (3 x 3)   e (5 x 7) – (2 x 5)
b (3 x 5) + (3 x 2)   d (2 x 5) + (2 x 6)   f (6 +7) + (12 –2)

(c)

Errors on this page will most likely be the result of choosing the wrong order of operation. Remind children that they must work out the brackets first, before they add or subtract the results. Concentration and careful reading should prevent any problems.

Simple use of brackets

Work out these sums.
(3 + 2) x (4 + 1) =   5 x 5 = 25
(10 x 5) ÷ (10 – 5) =   50 ÷ 5 = 10
Remember to work out the brackets first.

Work out these sums.

(7 + 3) x (8 – 4) =   40   (5 – 2) x (8 – 1) =   21

(9 + 5) ÷ (1 + 6) =   2   (14 – 6) x (4 + 3) =   56

(14 + 4) ÷ (12 – 6) =   3   (9 + 21) ÷ (8 – 5) =   10

(11 – 5) x (7 + 5) =   72   (8 + 20) ÷ (12 – 10) =   14

(6 + 9) ÷ (8 – 3) =   3   (14 – 3) x (6 + 1) =   77

(10 + 10) ÷ (2 + 3) =   4   (9 + 3) x (2 + 4) =   72

Now try these.

(4 x 3) ÷ (1 x 2) =   6   (5 x 4) ÷ (2 x 2) =   5

(8 x 5) ÷ (4 x 1) =   10   (6 x 4) ÷ (3 x 4) =   2

(2 x 4) x (2 x 3) =   48   (3 x 5) x (1 x 2) =   30

(8 x 4) ÷ (2 x 2) =   8   (6 x 4) ÷ (4 x 2) =   3

If the answer is 30, which of these sums gives the correct answer?
a (3 x 5) x (2 x 2)   d (20 ÷ 2) x (12 ÷ 3)
b (4 x 5) x (5 x 2)   e (5 x 12) ÷ (2 x 5)
c (12 x 5) ÷ (8 ÷ 4)   f (9 x 5) ÷ (10 ÷ 2)   c

If the answer is 8, which of these sums gives the correct answer?
a (16 ÷ 2) ÷ (2 x 1)   d (24 ÷ 6) x (8 ÷ 4)
b (9 ÷ 3) x (3 x 2)   e (8 ÷ 4) x (8 ÷ 1)
c (12 x 4) ÷ (6 x 2)   f (16 ÷ 4) x (20 ÷ 4)   d

This page continues the work of the previous page, but the brackets are multiplied or divided. It may be necessary to remind children to read carefully, as several operations take place in each sum.

17 — Simple use of brackets

Work out these sums.
$(5 + 3) + (9 - 2) =$ $8 + 7 = 15$
$(5 + 2) - (4 - 1) =$ $7 - 3 = 4$
$(4 + 2) \times (3 + 1) =$ $6 \times 4 = 24$
$(3 \times 5) \div (9 - 6) =$ $15 \div 3 = 5$
Remember to work out the brackets first.

Work out these sums.

$(5 + 4) + (7 - 3) =$	13	$(9 - 2) + (6 + 4) =$	17
$(7 + 3) - (9 - 7) =$	8	$(15 - 5) + (2 + 3) =$	15
$(11 \times 2) - (3 \times 2) =$	16	$(15 \div 3) + (9 \times 2) =$	23
$(12 \times 2) - (3 \times 3) =$	15	$(6 \div 2) + (8 \times 2) =$	19
$(9 \times 3) - (7 \times 3) =$	6	$(15 \div 5) + (3 \times 4) =$	15
$(20 \div 5) - (8 \div 2) =$	0	$(5 \times 10) - (12 \times 4) =$	2

Now try these.

$(4 + 8) \div (3 \times 2) =$	2	$(6 \times 4) \div (3 \times 2) =$	4
$(9 + 5) \div (2 \times 1) =$	7	$(7 \times 4) \div (3 + 4) =$	4
$(3 + 6) \times (3 \times 3) =$	81	$(5 \times 5) \div (10 \div 2) =$	5
$(24 \div 2) \times (3 \times 2) =$	72	$(8 \times 6) \div (2 \times 12) =$	2

Write down the letters of all the sums that make 25.
a $(2 \times 5) \times (3 \times 2)$ d $(40 \div 2) + (10 \div 2)$
b $(5 \times 5) + (7 - 2)$ e $(10 \times 5) - (5 \times 5)$
c $(6 \times 5) - (10 \div 2)$ f $(10 \times 10) \div (10 - 6)$ c, d, e, f

Write down the letters of all the sums that make 20.
a $(10 \div 2) \times (4 \div 4)$ d $(20 \div 4) \times (8 + 2)$
b $(7 \times 3) - (3 \div 3)$ e $(10 \div 2) + (20 \div 2)$
c $(8 \times 4) - (6 \times 2)$ f $(14 \div 2) + (2 \times 7)$ b, c

This page reinforces all the elements of the previous two pages. Again, the most likely cause of error will be lack of concentration.

18 — Multiplying decimals

Work out these sums.

4.6	3.9	8.4
x 3	x 5	x 8
13.8	19.5	67.2

Work out these sums.

4.7 x 3	9.1 x 3	5.8 x 3	1.7 x 2	5.1 x 2
14.1	27.3	17.4	3.4	10.2
7.4 x 2	3.6 x 4	6.5 x 4	4.2 x 2	3.8 x 2
14.8	14.4	26.0	8.4	7.6
4.2 x 4	4.7 x 4	1.8 x 5	3.4 x 5	3.7 x 5
16.8	18.8	9.0	17.0	18.5
2.5 x 5	2.4 x 6	5.3 x 7	7.2 x 8	5.1 x 9
12.5	14.4	37.1	57.6	45.9
7.9 x 9	8.6 x 9	8.8 x 8	7.5 x 8	9.9 x 6
71.1	77.4	70.4	60.0	59.4
6.8 x 7	5.7 x 6	6.9 x 7	7.5 x 9	8.4 x 9
47.6	34.2	48.3	67.5	75.6
7.3 x 8	2.8 x 7	3.8 x 8	7.7 x 7	9.4 x 9
58.4	19.6	30.4	53.9	84.6

Ensure that children work from right to left. Problems will highlight gaps in their knowledge of times tables. Remind them that the number they are multiplying has one decimal place, so their answer must have one decimal place also, and this can be put in at the end.

19 — Multiplying decimals

Work out these sums.

37.5	26.2	65.3
x 2	x 5	x 9
75.0	131.0	587.7

Work out these sums.

53.3 x 2	93.2 x 2	51.4 x 2	34.6 x 3	35.2 x 3
106.6	186.4	102.8	103.8	105.6
46.5 x 4	25.8 x 4	16.4 x 3	47.1 x 5	37.4 x 5
186.0	103.2	49.2	235.5	187.0
12.4 x 5	46.3 x 5	17.5 x 6	36.5 x 6	72.4 x 7
62.0	231.5	105.0	219.0	506.8
37.5 x 7	20.3 x 7	73.4 x 7	92.6 x 6	47.9 x 6
262.5	142.1	513.8	555.6	287.4
53.9 x 8	75.6 x 8	28.8 x 8	79.4 x 8	99.9 x 9
431.2	604.8	230.4	635.2	899.1
37.9 x 9	14.8 x 9	35.4 x 9	46.8 x 8	27.2 x 7
341.1	133.2	318.6	374.4	190.4
39.5 x 6	84.2 x 9	68.5 x 8	73.2 x 9	47.6 x 6
237.0	757.8	548.0	658.8	285.6

This page further revises decimal multiplication, using larger numbers.

20 — Real life problems

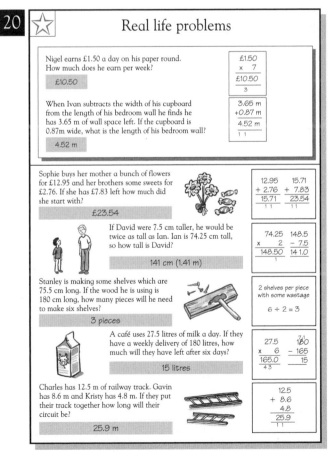

Nigel earns £1.50 a day on his paper round. How much does he earn per week?
£10.50

£1.50
x 7
£10.50

When Ivan subtracts the width of his cupboard from the length of his bedroom wall he finds he has 3.65 m of wall space left. If the cupboard is 0.87m wide, what is the length of his bedroom wall?
4.52 m

3.65 m
+0.87 m
4.52 m

Sophie buys her mother a bunch of flowers for £12.95 and her brothers some sweets for £2.76. If she has £7.83 left how much did she start with?
£23.54

12.95	15.71
+ 2.76	+ 7.83
15.71	23.54

If David were 7.5 cm taller, he would be twice as tall as Ian. Ian is 74.25 cm tall, so how tall is David?
141 cm (1.41 m)

74.25	148.5
x 2	- 7.5
148.50	141.0

Stanley is making some shelves which are 75.5 cm long. If the wood he is using is 180 cm long, how many pieces will he need to make six shelves?
3 pieces

2 shelves per piece with some wastage
$6 \div 2 = 3$

A café uses 27.5 litres of milk a day. If they have a weekly delivery of 180 litres, how much will they have left after six days?
15 litres

27.5	180
x 6	- 165
165.0	15

Charles has 12.5 m of railway track. Gavin has 8.6 m and Kristy has 4.8 m. If they put their track together how long will their circuit be?
25.9 m

12.5
+ 8.6
4.8
25.9

This page provides an opportunity to apply the skills practised to real life problems. Children will need to choose the operation carefully. Some questions require more than one operation.

Real life problems

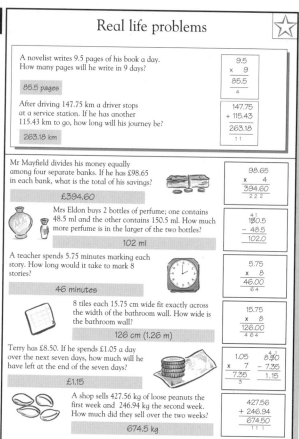

A novelist writes 9.5 pages of his book a day. How many pages will he write in 9 days?

85.5 pages

$$\begin{array}{r} 9.5 \\ \times\ \ 9 \\ \hline 85.5 \\ \tiny 4 \end{array}$$

After driving 147.75 km a driver stops at a service station. If he has another 115.43 km to go, how long will his journey be?

263.18 km

$$\begin{array}{r} 147.75 \\ +\ 115.43 \\ \hline 263.18 \\ \tiny 1\ 1 \end{array}$$

Mr Mayfield divides his money equally among four separate banks. If he has £98.65 in each bank, what is the total of his savings?

£394.60

$$\begin{array}{r} 98.65 \\ \times\ \ \ 4 \\ \hline 394.60 \\ \tiny 2\ 2\ 2 \end{array}$$

Mrs Eldon buys 2 bottles of perfume; one contains 48.5 ml and the other contains 150.5 ml. How much more perfume is in the larger of the two bottles?

102 ml

$$\begin{array}{r} 150.5 \\ -\ \ 48.5 \\ \hline 102.0 \end{array}$$

A teacher spends 5.75 minutes marking each story. How long would it take to mark 8 stories?

46 minutes

$$\begin{array}{r} 5.75 \\ \times\ \ 8 \\ \hline 46.00 \\ \tiny 6\ 4 \end{array}$$

8 tiles each 15.75 cm wide fit exactly across the width of the bathroom wall. How wide is the bathroom wall?

126 cm (1.26 m)

$$\begin{array}{r} 15.75 \\ \times\ \ 8 \\ \hline 126.00 \\ \tiny 4\ 6\ 4 \end{array}$$

Terry has £8.50. If he spends £1.05 a day over the next seven days, how much will he have left at the end of the seven days?

£1.15

$$\begin{array}{r} 1.05 \\ \times\ \ 7 \\ \hline 7.35 \\ \tiny 3 \end{array} \qquad \begin{array}{r} 8.50 \\ -\ 7.35 \\ \hline 1.15 \end{array}$$

A shop sells 427.56 kg of loose peanuts the first week and 246.94 kg the second week. How much did they sell over the two weeks?

674.5 kg

$$\begin{array}{r} 427.56 \\ +\ 246.94 \\ \hline 674.50 \\ \tiny 1\ 1\ 1 \end{array}$$

Another page that revises various operations in real life situations.

Real life problems

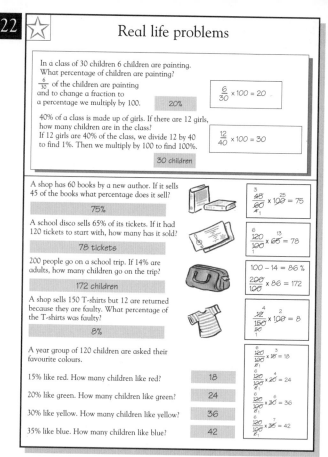

In a class of 30 children 6 children are painting. What percentage of children are painting? $\frac{6}{30}$ of the children are painting and to change a fraction to a percentage we multiply by 100.

20%

$$\frac{6}{30} \times 100 = 20$$

40% of a class is made up of girls. If there are 12 girls, how many children are in the class? If 12 girls are 40% of the class, we divide 12 by 40 to find 1%. Then we multiply by 100 to find 100%.

30 children

$$\frac{12}{40} \times 100 = 30$$

A shop has 60 books by a new author. If it sells 45 of the books what percentage does it sell?

75%

$$\frac{\overset{3}{\cancel{45}}}{\underset{4}{\cancel{60}}} \times \overset{25}{\cancel{100}}\ _{1} = 75$$

A school disco sells 65% of its tickets. If it had 120 tickets to start with, how many has it sold?

78 tickets

$$\frac{120}{100} \times \overset{13}{\cancel{65}} = 78$$

200 people go on a school trip. If 14% are adults, how many children go on the trip?

172 children

$$100 - 14 = 86\ \%$$
$$\frac{200}{100} \times 86 = 172$$

A shop sells 150 T-shirts but 12 are returned because they are faulty. What percentage of the T-shirts was faulty?

8%

$$\frac{\overset{4}{\cancel{12}}}{\underset{30}{\cancel{150}}} \times \overset{2}{\cancel{100}} = 8$$

A year group of 120 children are asked their favourite colours.

15% like red. How many children like red? **18**

$$\frac{120}{100} \times \overset{3}{\cancel{15}} = 18$$

20% like green. How many children like green? **24**

$$\frac{120}{100} \times \overset{4}{\cancel{20}} = 24$$

30% like yellow. How many children like yellow? **36**

$$\frac{120}{100} \times \overset{6}{\cancel{30}} = 36$$

35% like blue. How many children like blue? **42**

$$\frac{120}{100} \times \overset{7}{\cancel{35}} = 42$$

In questions 1 and 4 children should see that the answer can be expressed as a fraction, which can then be converted to a percentage by multiplying by 100.

Comparing units

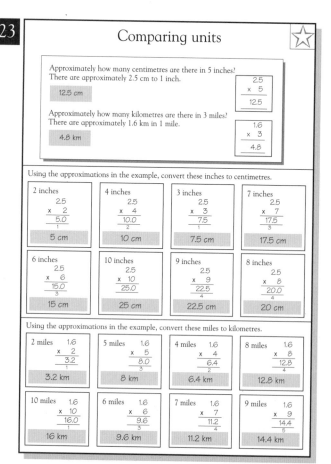

Approximately how many centimetres are there in 5 inches? There are approximately 2.5 cm to 1 inch.

12.5 cm

$$\begin{array}{r} 2.5 \\ \times\ \ 5 \\ \hline 12.5 \end{array}$$

Approximately how many kilometres are there in 3 miles? There are approximately 1.6 km in 1 mile.

4.8 km

$$\begin{array}{r} 1.6 \\ \times\ \ 3 \\ \hline 4.8 \end{array}$$

Using the approximations in the example, convert these inches to centimetres.

2 inches
$$\begin{array}{r} 2.5 \\ \times\ \ 2 \\ \hline 5.0 \\ \tiny 1 \end{array}$$
5 cm

4 inches
$$\begin{array}{r} 2.5 \\ \times\ \ 4 \\ \hline 10.0 \\ \tiny 2 \end{array}$$
10 cm

3 inches
$$\begin{array}{r} 2.5 \\ \times\ \ 3 \\ \hline 7.5 \\ \tiny 1 \end{array}$$
7.5 cm

7 inches
$$\begin{array}{r} 2.5 \\ \times\ \ 7 \\ \hline 17.5 \\ \tiny 3 \end{array}$$
17.5 cm

6 inches
$$\begin{array}{r} 2.5 \\ \times\ \ 6 \\ \hline 15.0 \\ \tiny 3 \end{array}$$
15 cm

10 inches
$$\begin{array}{r} 2.5 \\ \times\ \ 10 \\ \hline 25.0 \end{array}$$
25 cm

9 inches
$$\begin{array}{r} 2.5 \\ \times\ \ 9 \\ \hline 22.5 \\ \tiny 4 \end{array}$$
22.5 cm

8 inches
$$\begin{array}{r} 2.5 \\ \times\ \ 8 \\ \hline 20.0 \\ \tiny 4 \end{array}$$
20 cm

Using the approximations in the example, convert these miles to kilometres.

2 miles
$$\begin{array}{r} 1.6 \\ \times\ \ 2 \\ \hline 3.2 \end{array}$$
3.2 km

5 miles
$$\begin{array}{r} 1.6 \\ \times\ \ 5 \\ \hline 8.0 \\ \tiny 3 \end{array}$$
8 km

4 miles
$$\begin{array}{r} 1.6 \\ \times\ \ 4 \\ \hline 6.4 \\ \tiny 2 \end{array}$$
6.4 km

8 miles
$$\begin{array}{r} 1.6 \\ \times\ \ 8 \\ \hline 12.8 \\ \tiny 4 \end{array}$$
12.8 km

10 miles
$$\begin{array}{r} 1.6 \\ \times\ \ 10 \\ \hline 16.0 \\ \tiny 1 \end{array}$$
16 km

6 miles
$$\begin{array}{r} 1.6 \\ \times\ \ 6 \\ \hline 9.6 \\ \tiny 3 \end{array}$$
9.6 km

7 miles
$$\begin{array}{r} 1.6 \\ \times\ \ 7 \\ \hline 11.2 \\ \tiny 4 \end{array}$$
11.2 km

9 miles
$$\begin{array}{r} 1.6 \\ \times\ \ 9 \\ \hline 14.4 \\ \tiny 5 \end{array}$$
14.4 km

This page and the next should be fairly straightforward as children are given the conversion factors. Notice that they are required to multiply decimals, which has been practised earlier in this book. It is worth pointing out that these conversions are approximate.

Comparing units

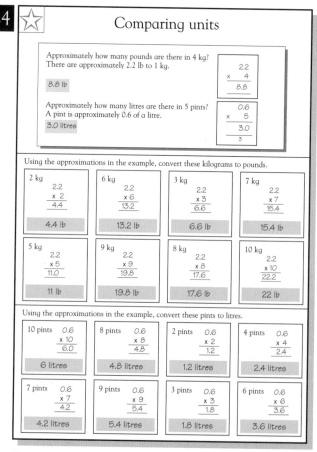

Approximately how many pounds are there in 4 kg? There are approximately 2.2 lb to 1 kg.

8.8 lb

$$\begin{array}{r} 2.2 \\ \times\ \ 4 \\ \hline 8.8 \end{array}$$

Approximately how many litres are there in 5 pints? A pint is approximately 0.6 of a litre.

3.0 litres

$$\begin{array}{r} 0.6 \\ \times\ \ 5 \\ \hline 3.0 \\ \tiny 3 \end{array}$$

Using the approximations in the example, convert these kilograms to pounds.

2 kg
$$\begin{array}{r} 2.2 \\ \times\ 2 \\ \hline 4.4 \end{array}$$
4.4 lb

6 kg
$$\begin{array}{r} 2.2 \\ \times\ 6 \\ \hline 13.2 \end{array}$$
13.2 lb

3 kg
$$\begin{array}{r} 2.2 \\ \times\ 3 \\ \hline 6.6 \end{array}$$
6.6 lb

7 kg
$$\begin{array}{r} 2.2 \\ \times\ 7 \\ \hline 15.4 \end{array}$$
15.4 lb

5 kg
$$\begin{array}{r} 2.2 \\ \times\ 5 \\ \hline 11.0 \end{array}$$
11 lb

9 kg
$$\begin{array}{r} 2.2 \\ \times\ 9 \\ \hline 19.8 \end{array}$$
19.8 lb

8 kg
$$\begin{array}{r} 2.2 \\ \times\ 8 \\ \hline 17.6 \end{array}$$
17.6 lb

10 kg
$$\begin{array}{r} 2.2 \\ \times\ 10 \\ \hline 22.2 \end{array}$$
22 lb

Using the approximations in the example, convert these pints to litres.

10 pints
$$\begin{array}{r} 0.6 \\ \times\ 10 \\ \hline 6.0 \end{array}$$
6 litres

8 pints
$$\begin{array}{r} 0.6 \\ \times\ 8 \\ \hline 4.8 \end{array}$$
4.8 litres

2 pints
$$\begin{array}{r} 0.6 \\ \times\ 2 \\ \hline 1.2 \end{array}$$
1.2 litres

4 pints
$$\begin{array}{r} 0.6 \\ \times\ 4 \\ \hline 2.4 \end{array}$$
2.4 litres

7 pints
$$\begin{array}{r} 0.6 \\ \times\ 7 \\ \hline 4.2 \end{array}$$
4.2 litres

9 pints
$$\begin{array}{r} 0.6 \\ \times\ 9 \\ \hline 5.4 \end{array}$$
5.4 litres

3 pints
$$\begin{array}{r} 0.6 \\ \times\ 3 \\ \hline 1.8 \end{array}$$
1.8 litres

6 pints
$$\begin{array}{r} 0.6 \\ \times\ 6 \\ \hline 3.6 \end{array}$$
3.6 litres

Once again children are required to multiply decimals, which has been practised earlier in the book. It is worth pointing out that these conversions are approximate.

Area of basic compound shapes

Find the area of this shape.

To find the area of this shape we divide it into 2 rectangles and add the two areas together.

1036 cm²

8 cm

B

25 cm   A   42 cm

36 cm

A = 25
× 36
750
150
900 cm²

B = 17
× 8
136 cm²

900
+ 136
1036 cm²

Find the area of these shapes.

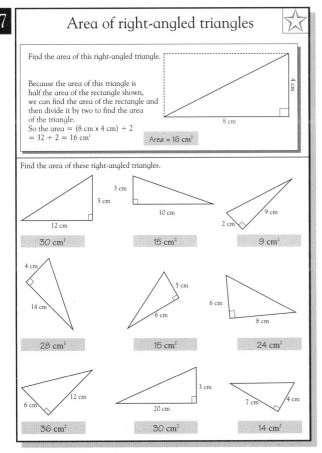

4 cm

20 cm

2 cm

20 cm

20 16 80
× 4 × 2 +32
80 32 112

112 cm²

15 cm

2 cm

8 cm

2 cm

15 8   30
× 2 × 2 +16
30 16 46

46 cm²

40 cm

35 cm   10 cm

85 cm

85   25
× 10 × 40
850 1000

850
+ 1000
1850

1850 cm²

8 cm

9 cm

2 cm

19 cm

9 × 8 = 72

19   38
× 2 + 72
38   110

110 cm²

3 cm   2 cm

22 cm   25 cm

48 cm

48   22
× 3 × 3
144 66

144   22 + 66
2   22   44
× 2 44
44   254

254 cm²

10 cm

2 cm

5 cm

15 cm   5 cm

4 cm

10 cm

10   9 × 5 = 45
× 4 10 × 2 = 20
40

40
+ 45
20
105

105 cm²

The most likely difficulties will come in deciding how to split the shapes. Give assistance in finding a way of splitting the shape so that children get the dimensions necessary to do the calculations. There are several ways of dividing most of the shapes.

Area of basic compound shapes

Find the area of this shape.

To find the area of this shape we divide it into 2 rectangles and add the two areas together.

15 cm

18 cm   42 cm

A   B   21 cm

1467 cm²

A = 15
× 39
450
135
585 cm²

B = 42
× 21
840
42
882 cm²

882
+ 585
1467 cm²

Find the area of each shape.

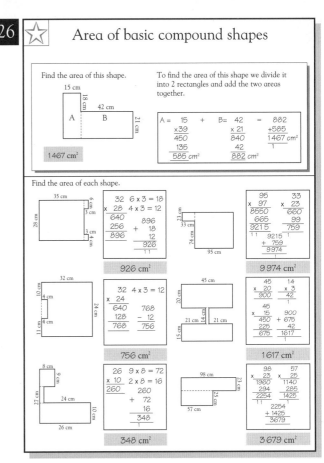

35 cm

28 cm   6 cm
3 cm
3 cm
4 cm

32   6 × 3 = 18
× 28 4 × 3 = 12
640
256   896
896   + 18
12
926

926 cm²

95
× 97
8550
665
9215

33
× 23
660
99
759

9215
+ 759
9974

9974 cm²

32 cm

10 cm
4 cm

11 cm   4 cm

24 cm

32   4 × 3 = 12
× 24
640   768
128   − 12
768   756

756 cm²

45 cm

20 cm

21 cm 14 cm 21 cm

15 cm

45   14
× 20 × 3
900   42

45
× 15 900
450 + 675
225 1617
675

1617 cm²

8 cm

9 cm

27 cm

24 cm

26 cm

10 cm

26   9 × 8 = 72
× 10 2 × 8 = 16
260
260
+ 72
16
348

348 cm²

98 cm

23 cm

25 cm

57 cm

98   57
× 23 × 25
1960 1140
294   285
2254 1425

2254
+ 1425
3679

3679 cm²

Once again the most likely difficulties will come in deciding how to split the shapes, so help the children to choose the method they find easiest.

Area of right-angled triangles

Find the area of this right-angled triangle.

Because the area of this triangle is half the area of the rectangle shown, we can find the area of the rectangle and then divide it by two to find the area of the triangle.
So the area = (8 cm × 4 cm) ÷ 2
= 32 ÷ 2 = 16 cm²

4 cm

8 cm

Area = 16 cm²

Find the area of these right-angled triangles.

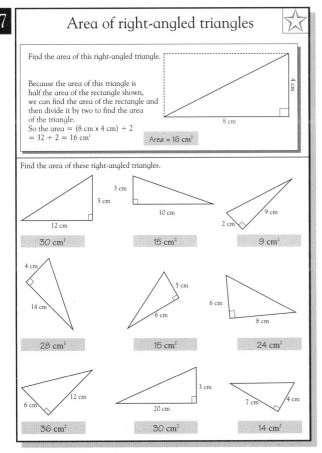

5 cm

12 cm

30 cm²

3 cm

10 cm

15 cm²

9 cm

2 cm

9 cm²

4 cm

14 cm

28 cm²

5 cm

6 cm

15 cm²

6 cm

8 cm

24 cm²

12 cm

6 cm

36 cm²

3 cm

20 cm

30 cm²

7 cm   4 cm

14 cm²

The operation of multiplying the sides together and dividing by two should offer no serious difficulty to children, but make sure that they are really clear about why they are doing this.

Speed problems

How long would it take to travel 120 km at 8 kph?
(Time = Distance ÷ Speed)

15 hours

15
8)120

If a lorry takes 3 hours to travel 150 km, how fast is it going?
(Speed = Distance ÷ Time)

50 kph

50
3)150

If a car travels at 60 kph for 2 hours, how far has it gone?
(Distance = Speed × Time)

120 km

60
× 2
120

If a man walks for 3 kilometres at a steady speed of 6 kph, how long will it take him?

30 mins

$\frac{3}{6} = \frac{1}{2}$

= 30 mins

A lorry driver travels 120 km in 3 hours. If he drove at a steady speed how fast was he going?

40 kph

40
3)120

A car travels at a steady speed of 90 kph. How far will it travel in 4 hours?

360 km

90
× 4
360

Shane walks 10 km at 4 kph. Damien walks 12 km at 5 kph. Which of them will take the longest?

Shane

Shane 4)10 2½
Damien 5)12
2½ is longer than 2⅖

Courtney drives for 30 minutes at 80 kph and for 1 hour at 60 kph. How far has he travelled altogether?

100 km

40   + 1 × 60
2)80   40
+ 60
100

A racing car travels 60 km in 20 minutes. What speed is it travelling at?

180 kph

60
× 3
180

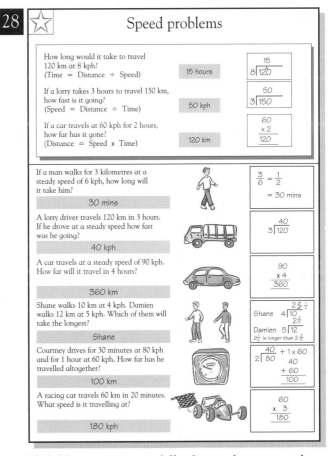

If children experience difficulty on this page, ask them what they need to find, speed, distance or time, and refer them to the necessary formula. Encourage them to develop simple examples which will help them to remember the formulae.

Probability scale 0 to 1

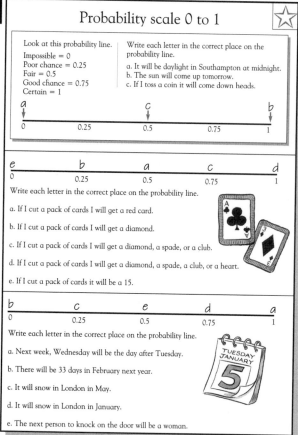

Look at this probability line.

Impossible = 0
Poor chance = 0.25
Fair = 0.5
Good chance = 0.75
Certain = 1

Write each letter in the correct place on the probability line.

a. It will be daylight in Southampton at midnight.
b. The sun will come up tomorrow.
c. If I toss a coin it will come down heads.

a .... c .... b

0 ...... 0.25 ...... 0.5 ...... 0.75 1

e ...... b ...... a ...... c ...... d

0 ...... 0.25 ...... 0.5 ...... 0.75 1

Write each letter in the correct place on the probability line.

a. If I cut a pack of cards I will get a red card.

b. If I cut a pack of cards I will get a diamond.

c. If I cut a pack of cards I will get a diamond, a spade, or a club.

d. If I cut a pack of cards I will get a diamond, a spade, a club, or a heart.

e. If I cut a pack of cards it will be a 15.

b ...... c ...... e ...... d ...... a

0 ...... 0.25 ...... 0.5 ...... 0.75 1

Write each letter in the correct place on the probability line.

a. Next week, Wednesday will be the day after Tuesday.

b. There will be 33 days in February next year.

c. It will snow in London in May.

d. It will snow in London in January.

e. The next person to knock on the door will be a woman.

The first section presupposes a knowledge of the suits of a pack of cards. If the child is unfamiliar with cards some discussion will be necessary. In the second section the examples have been chosen to fall fairly firmly into the categories listed on the probability line.

Interpreting pie charts

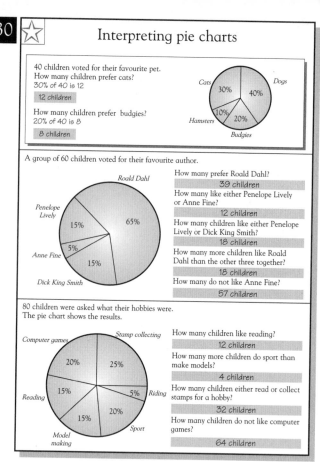

40 children voted for their favourite pet.
How many children prefer cats?
30% of 40 is 12

12 children

How many children prefer budgies?
20% of 40 is 8

8 children

A group of 60 children voted for their favourite author.

How many prefer Roald Dahl?
39 children

How many like either Penelope Lively or Anne Fine?
12 children

How many children like either Penelope Lively or Dick King Smith?
18 children

How many more children like Roald Dahl than the other three together?
18 children

How many do not like Anne Fine?
57 children

80 children were asked what their hobbies were. The pie chart shows the results.

How many children like reading?
12 children

How many more children do sport than make models?
4 children

How many children either read or collect stamps for a hobby?
32 children

How many children do not like computer games?
64 children

On this page children have to find percentages of amounts. If they are unsure, remind them to divide the amount by 100, so producing a fraction, and then multiply by the required percentage.

Likely outcomes

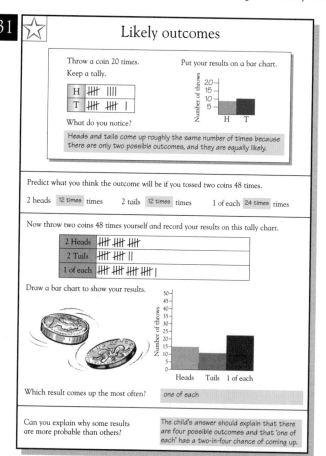

Throw a coin 20 times. Keep a tally.

| H | ﬘ IIII |
| T | ﬘ ﬘ I |

Put your results on a bar chart.

What do you notice?

Heads and tails come up roughly the same number of times because there are only two possible outcomes, and they are equally likely.

Predict what you think the outcome will be if you tossed two coins 48 times.

2 heads   12 times   times   2 tails   12 times   times   1 of each   24 times   times

Now throw two coins 48 times yourself and record your results on this tally chart.

2 Heads	﬘ ﬘ ﬘
2 Tails	﬘ ﬘ II
1 of each	﬘ ﬘ ﬘ ﬘ I

Draw a bar chart to show your results.

Which result comes up the most often?
one of each

Can you explain why some results are more probable than others?
The child's answer should explain that there are four possible outcomes and that 'one of each' has a two-in-four chance of coming up.

The child's prediction in the first question may be considerably different from the result. Once the work is done check that the child can use the experience to improve their understanding of likely outcomes. The tally chart may differ from the one shown here.

Drawing 2D shapes

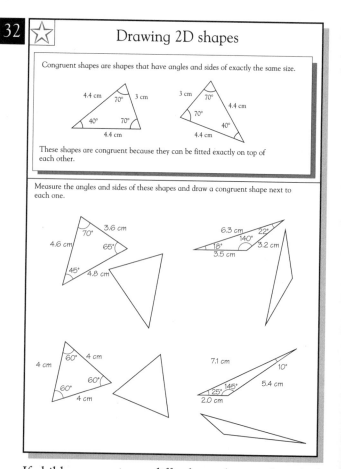

Congruent shapes are shapes that have angles and sides of exactly the same size.

These shapes are congruent because they can be fitted exactly on top of each other.

Measure the angles and sides of these shapes and draw a congruent shape next to each one.

If children experience difficulty with triangles, check the measurements of the angles and sides. It is better to avoid drawing a mirror image of the shape as the relationship between angles and sides may cause confusion.

Simple use of brackets

Work out these sums.

(5 + 3) + (9 − 2) = 8 + 7 = 15

(5 + 2) − (4 − 1) = 7 − 3 = 4

(4 + 2) x (3 + 1) = 6 x 4 = 24

(3 x 5) ÷ (9 − 6) = 15 ÷ 3 = 5

Remember to work out the brackets first.

Work out these sums.

(5 + 4) + (7 − 3) =

(7 + 3) − (9 − 7) =

(11 x 2) − (3 x 2) =

(12 x 2) − (3 x 3) =

(9 x 3) − (7 x 3) =

(20 ÷ 5) − (8 ÷ 2) =

(9 − 2) + (6 + 4) =

(15 − 5) + (2 + 3) =

(15 ÷ 3) + (9 x 2) =

(6 ÷ 2) + (8 x 2) =

(15 ÷ 5) + (3 x 4) =

(5 x 10) − (12 x 4) =

Now try these.

(4 + 8) ÷ (3 x 2) =

(9 + 5) ÷ (2 x 1) =

(3 + 6) x (3 x 3) =

(24 ÷ 2) x (3 x 2) =

(6 x 4) ÷ (3 x 2) =

(7 x 4) ÷ (3 + 4) =

(5 x 5) ÷ (10 ÷ 2) =

(8 x 6) ÷ (2 x 12) =

Write down the letters of all the sums that make 25.

a (2 x 5) x (3 x 2)

b (5 x 5) + (7 − 2)

c (6 x 5) − (10 ÷ 2)

d (40 ÷ 2) + (10 ÷ 2)

e (10 x 5) − (5 x 5)

f (10 x 10) ÷ (10 − 6)

Write down the letters of all the sums that make 20.

a (10 ÷ 2) x (4 ÷ 4)

b (7 x 3) − (3 ÷ 3)

c (8 x 4) − (6 x 2)

d (20 ÷ 4) x (8 + 2)

e (10 ÷ 2) + (20 ÷ 2)

f (14 ÷ 2) + (2 x 7)

Multiplying decimals

Work out these sums.

4.6	3.9	8.4
x 3	x 5	x 8
13.8	19.5	67.2
1	4	3

Work out these sums.

4.7	9.1	5.8	1.7	5.1
x 3	x 3	x 3	x 2	x 2

7.4	3.6	6.5	4.2	3.8
x 2	x 4	x 4	x 2	x 2

4.2	4.7	1.8	3.4	3.7
x 4	x 4	x 5	x 5	x 5

2.5	2.4	5.3	7.2	5.1
x 5	x 6	x 7	x 8	x 9

7.9	8.6	8.8	7.5	9.9
x 9	x 9	x 8	x 8	x 6

6.8	5.7	6.9	7.5	8.4
x 7	x 6	x 7	x 9	x 9

7.3	2.8	3.8	7.7	9.4
x 8	x 7	x 8	x 7	x 9

Multiplying decimals

Work out these sums.

37.5	26.2	65.3
x 2	x 5	x 9
75.0	131.0	587.7
1 1	3 1	4 2

Work out these sums.

53.3	93.2	51.4	34.6	35.2
x 2	x 2	x 2	x 3	x 3

46.5	25.8	16.4	47.1	37.4
x 4	x 4	x 3	x 5	x 5

12.4	46.3	17.5	36.5	72.4
x 5	x 5	x 6	x 6	x 7

37.5	20.3	73.4	92.6	47.9
x 7	x 7	x 7	x 6	x 6

53.9	75.6	28.8	79.4	99.9
x 8	x 8	x 8	x 8	x 9

37.9	14.8	35.4	46.8	27.2
x 9	x 9	x 9	x 8	x 7

39.5	84.2	68.5	73.2	47.6
x 6	x 9	x 8	x 9	x 6

Real life problems

Nigel earns £1.50 a day on his paper round. How much does he earn per week?

£10.50

£1.50
× 7
£10.50
3

When Ivan subtracts the width of his cupboard from the length of his bedroom wall he finds he has 3.65 m of wall space left. If the cupboard is 0.87 m wide, what is the length of his bedroom wall?

4.52 m

3.65 m
+0.87 m
4.52 m
1 1

Sophie buys her mother a bunch of flowers for £12.95 and her brothers some sweets for £2.76. If she has £7.83 left how much did she start with?

If David were 7.5 cm taller, he would be twice as tall as Ian. Ian is 74.25 cm tall, so how tall is David?

Stanley is making some shelves which are 75.5 cm long. If the wood he is using is 180 cm long, how many pieces will he need to make six shelves?

A café uses 27.5 litres of milk a day. If they have a weekly delivery of 180 litres, how much will they have left after six days?

Charles has 12.5 m of railway track. Gavin has 8.6 m and Kristy has 4.8 m. If they put their track together how long will their circuit be?

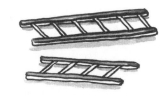

Real life problems

A novelist writes 9.5 pages of his book each day.
How many pages will he write in 9 days?

$$\begin{array}{r} 9.5 \\ \times 9 \\ \hline 85.5 \\ \hline 4 \end{array}$$

85.5 pages

After driving 147.75 km a driver stops
at a service station. If he has another
115.43 km to go, how long will his journey be?

$$\begin{array}{r} 147.75 \\ + 115.43 \\ \hline 263.18 \\ \hline 11 \end{array}$$

263.18 km

Mr Mayfield divides his money equally
among four separate banks. If he has £98.65
in each bank, what is the total of his savings?

Mrs Eldon buys 2 bottles of perfume; one contains
48.5 ml and the other contains 150.5 ml. How much
more perfume is in the larger of the two bottles?

A teacher spends 5.75 minutes marking
each story. How long would it take to
mark 8 stories?

8 tiles each 15.75 cm wide fit exactly across
the width of the bathroom wall. How wide is
the bathroom wall?

Terry has £8.50. If he spends £1.05 a day
over the next seven days, how much will he
have left at the end of the seven days?

A shop sells 427.56 kg of loose peanuts the
first week and 246.94 kg the second week.
How much did they sell over the two weeks?

21

Real life problems

In a class of 30 children 6 children are painting.
What percentage of children are painting?

$\frac{6}{30}$ of the children are painting
and to change a fraction to
a percentage we multiply by 100.

20%

$$\frac{6}{30} \times 100 = 20$$

40% of a class is made up of girls. If there are 12 girls,
how many children are in the class?
If 12 girls are 40% of the class, we divide 12 by 40
to find 1%. Then we multiply by 100 to find 100%.

30 children

$$\frac{12}{40} \times 100 = 30$$

A shop has 60 books by a new author. If it sells
45 of the books what percentage does it sell?

A school disco sells 65% of its tickets. If it had
120 tickets to start with, how many has it sold?

200 people go on a school trip. If 14% are
adults, how many children go on the trip?

A shop sells 150 T-shirts but 12 are returned
because they are faulty. What percentage of
the T-shirts was faulty?

A year group of 120 children are asked their
favourite colours.

15% like red. How many children like red?

20% like green. How many children like green?

30% like yellow. How many children like yellow?

35% like blue. How many children like blue?

Comparing units

Approximately how many centimetres are there in 5 inches?
There are approximately 2.5 cm to 1 inch.

| 12.5 cm |

```
    2.5
  ×   5
  ─────
   12.5
```

Approximately how many kilometres are there in 3 miles?
There are approximately 1.6 km in 1 mile.

| 4.8 km |

```
    1.6
  ×   3
  ─────
    4.8
```

Using the approximations in the example, convert these inches to centimetres.

| 2 inches | 4 inches | 3 inches | 7 inches |

| 6 inches | 10 inches | 9 inches | 8 inches |

Using the approximations in the example, convert these miles to kilometres.

| 2 miles | 5 miles | 4 miles | 8 miles |

| 10 miles | 6 miles | 7 miles | 9 miles |

23

Comparing units

Approximately how many pounds are there in 4 kg?
There are approximately 2.2 lb to 1 kg.

8.8 lb

$$\begin{array}{r} 2.2 \\ \times \quad 4 \\ \hline 8.8 \end{array}$$

Approximately how many litres are there in 5 pints?
A pint is approximately 0.6 of a litre.

3.0 litres

$$\begin{array}{r} 0.6 \\ \times \quad 5 \\ \hline 3.0 \\ \hline 3 \end{array}$$

Using the approximations in the example, convert these kilograms to pounds.

| 2 kg | 6 kg | 3 kg | 7 kg |

| 5 kg | 9 kg | 8 kg | 10 kg |

Using the approximations in the example, convert these pints to litres.

| 10 pints | 8 pints | 2 pints | 4 pints |

| 7 pints | 9 pints | 3 pints | 6 pints |

Area of basic compound shapes

Find the area of this shape.

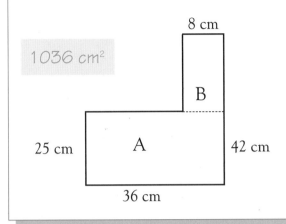

1036 cm²

8 cm

B

25 cm   A   42 cm

36 cm

To find the area of this shape we divide it into 2 rectangles and add the two areas together.

A=   25
     × 36
      750
      150
      900 cm²
        1

B =   17
     × 8
     136 cm²
        5

+

      900
   = +136
     1036 cm²

Find the area of these shapes.

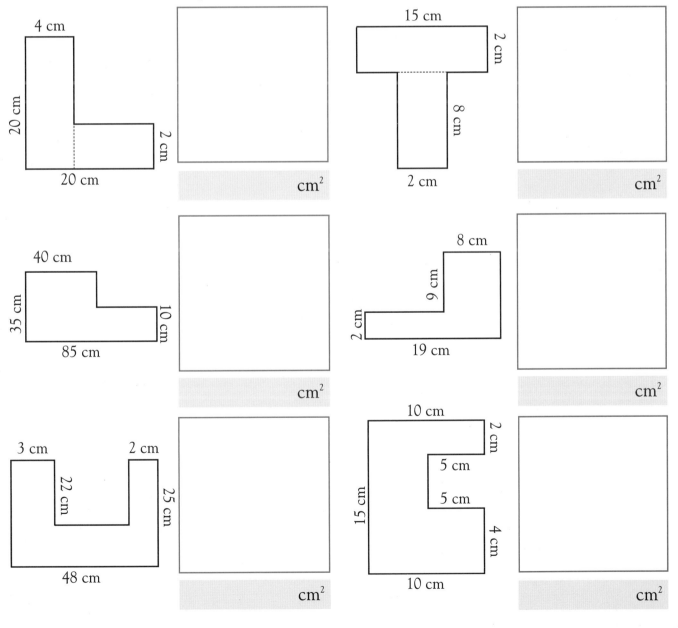

4 cm

20 cm

20 cm

2 cm

cm²

15 cm

2 cm

8 cm

2 cm

cm²

40 cm

35 cm

85 cm

10 cm

cm²

8 cm

9 cm

2 cm

19 cm

cm²

3 cm   2 cm

22 cm

25 cm

48 cm

cm²

10 cm

2 cm

5 cm

5 cm

15 cm

4 cm

10 cm

cm²

Area of basic compound shapes

Find the area of this shape.

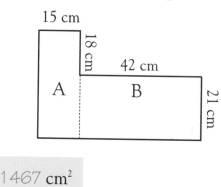

15 cm

18 cm

42 cm

A   B

21 cm

1467 cm²

To find the area of this shape we divide it into 2 rectangles and add the two areas together.

A =   15   +   B=   42   =   882
       ×39   × 21   +585
       450   840   1467 cm²
       135   42   1
       585 cm²   882 cm²

Find the area of each shape.

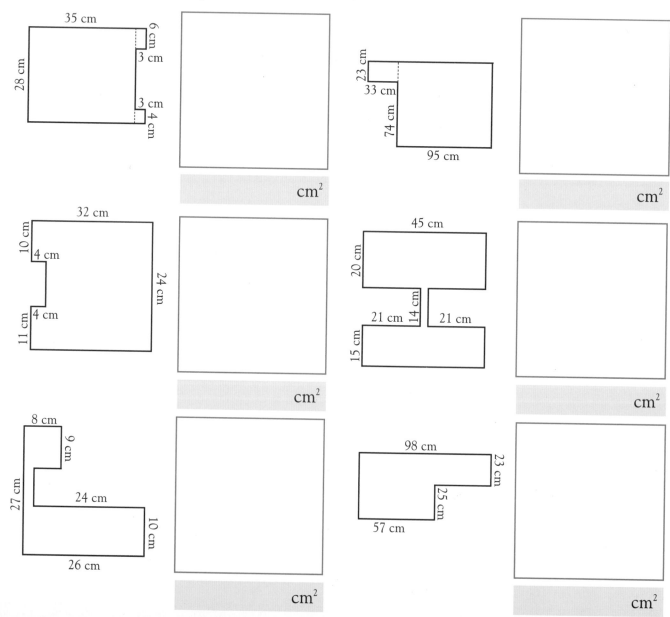

35 cm

6 cm

3 cm

28 cm

3 cm

4 cm

cm²

23 cm

33 cm

74 cm

95 cm

cm²

32 cm

10 cm

4 cm

24 cm

11 cm

4 cm

cm²

45 cm

20 cm

21 cm   14 cm   21 cm

15 cm

cm²

8 cm

9 cm

27 cm   24 cm

26 cm   10 cm

cm²

98 cm

23 cm

25 cm

57 cm

cm²

26

Area of right-angled triangles

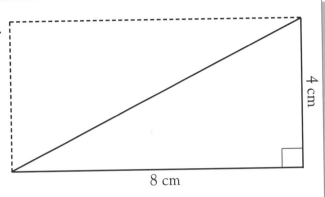

Find the area of this right-angled triangle.

Because the area of this triangle is
half the area of the rectangle shown,
we can find the area of the rectangle and
then divide it by two to find the area
of the triangle.

So the area = (8 cm × 4 cm) ÷ 2
= 32 ÷ 2 = 16 cm²

Area = 16 cm²

Find the areas of these right-angled triangles.

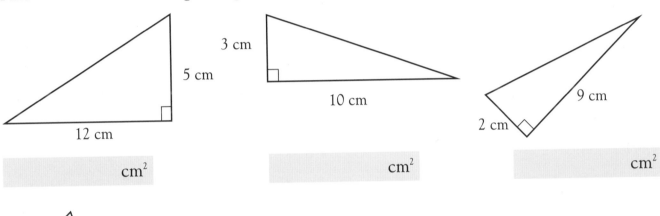

cm²

cm²

cm²

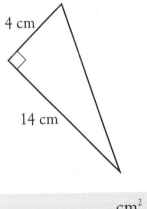

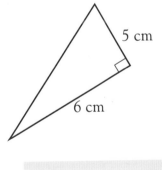

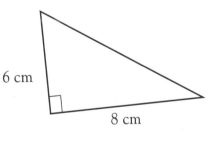

cm²

cm²

cm²

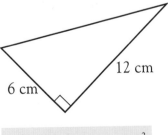

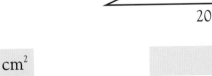

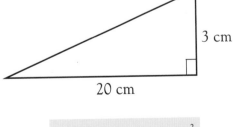

cm²

cm²

cm²

Speed problems

How long would it take to travel
120 km at 8 kph?
(Time = Distance ÷ Speed)

15 hours

If a lorry takes 3 hours to travel 150 km,
how fast is it going?
(Speed = Distance ÷ Time)

50 kph

If a car travels at 60 kph for 2 hours,
how far has it gone?
(Distance = Speed x Time)

120 km

If a man walks for 3 kilometres at a
steady speed of 6 kph, how long will
it take him?

A lorry driver travels 120 km in 3 hours.
If he drove at a steady speed how fast
was he going?

A car travels at a steady speed of 90 kph.
How far will it travel in 4 hours?

Shane walks 10 km at 4 kph. Damien
walks 12 km at 5 kph. Which of them will
take the longest?

Courtney drives for 30 minutes at 80 kph
and for 1 hour at 60 kph. How far has he
travelled altogether?

A racing car travels 60 km in 20 minutes.
What speed is it travelling at?

Probability scale 0 to 1

Look at this probability line.

Impossible = 0
Poor chance = 0.25
Fair = 0.5
Good chance = 0.75
Certain = 1

Write each letter in the correct place on the probability line.

a. It will be daylight in Southampton at midnight.
b. The sun will come up tomorrow.
c. If I toss a coin it will come down heads.

```
a                              c                              b
↓                              ↓                              ↓
|_____
0           0.25            0.5            0.75            1
```

```
|_____
0           0.25            0.5            0.75            1
```

Write each letter in the correct place on the probability line.

a. If I cut a pack of cards I will get a red card.

b. If I cut a pack of cards I will get a diamond.

c. If I cut a pack of cards I will get a diamond, a spade, or a club.

d. If I cut a pack of cards I will get a diamond, a spade, a club, or a heart.

e. If I cut a pack of cards it will be a 15.

```
|_____
0           0.25            0.5            0.75            1
```

Write each letter in the correct place on the probability line.

a. Next week, Wednesday will be the day after Tuesday.

b. There will be 33 days in February next year.

c. It will snow in London in May.

d. It will snow in London in January.

e. The next person to knock on the door will be a woman.

Interpreting pie charts

40 children voted for their favourite pet.
How many children prefer cats?
30% of 40 is 12

12 children

How many children prefer budgies?
20% of 40 is 8

8 children

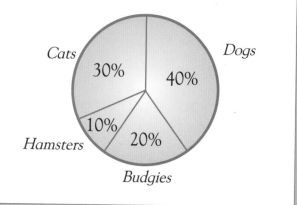

A group of 60 children voted for their favourite author.

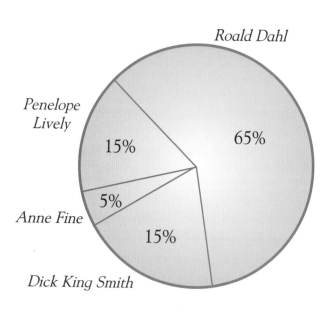

How many prefer Roald Dahl?

How many like either Penelope Lively or Anne Fine?

How many children like either Penelope Lively or Dick King Smith?

How many more children like Roald Dahl than the other three together?

How many do not like Anne Fine?

80 children were asked what their hobbies were.
The pie chart shows the results.

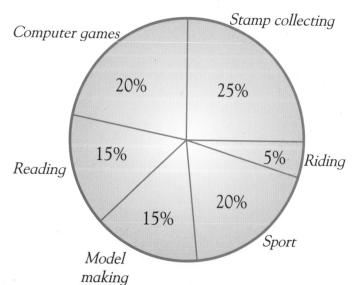

How many children like reading?

How many more children do sport than make models?

How many children either read or collect stamps for a hobby?

How many children do not like computer games?

Likely outcomes

Throw a coin 20 times.
Keep a tally.

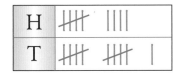

H	☰ ☰ ‖‖‖
T	☰ ☰ ☰ ☰ ‖

What do you notice?

Put your results on a bar chart.

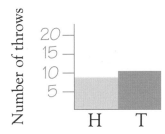

Heads and tails come up roughly the same number of times because there are only two possible outcomes, and they are equally likely.

Predict what you think the outcome would be if you tossed two coins 48 times.

2 heads   times   2 tails   times   1 of each   times

Now throw two coins 48 times yourself and record your results on this tally chart.

2 Heads	
2 Tails	
1 of each	

Draw a bar chart to show your results.

Which result comes up the most often?

Can you explain why some results
are more probable than others?

31

Drawing 2D shapes

Congruent shapes are shapes that have angles and sides of exactly the same size.

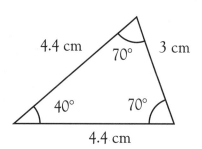

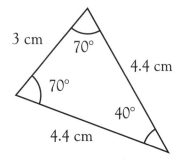

These shapes are congruent because they can be fitted exactly on top of each other.

Measure the angles and sides of these shapes and draw a congruent shape next to each one.

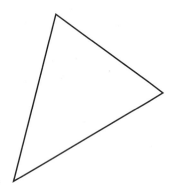

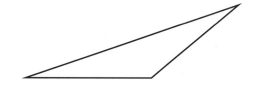

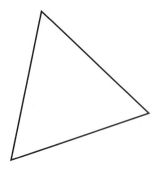

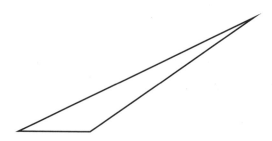